Student Activities Manual

to accompany

ADJUSTMENT AND GROWTH:

THE CHALLENGES OF LIFE

Sixth Edition

by

Spencer A. Rathus

and

Jeffrey S. Nevid

Gary W. Piggrem
DeVry Institute of Technology
Columbus, Ohio

James O. Davis
Southwest Missouri State University
Springfield, Missouri

Harcourt Brace College Publishers

Fort Worth • Philadelphia • San Diego • New York • Orlando • Austin • San Antonio
Toronto • Montreal • London • Sydney • Tokyo

Address Editorial Correspondence To:
Harcourt Brace College Publishers
301 Commerce Street, Suite 3700
Fort Worth, TX 76102

Address Orders To:
Harcourt Brace & Company
6277 Sea Harbor Drive
Orlando, FL 32887-6777
1-800-782-4479 or 1-800-433-0001 (in Florida)

Printed in the United States of America

ISBN: 0-15-503126-0

4 5 6 7 8 9 0 1 2 3 066 9 8 7 6 5 4 3 2 1

TABLE OF CONTENTS

PREFACE

Socrates was considered an effective teacher because he asked his listeners to participate in the learning process. He simply asked provocative and leading questions, and as the answers were developed, the students grew in knowledge and wisdom. Most of us enjoy the opportunity to discover by doing and by experiencing because we find it makes learning more exciting and the lessons more useful. The simple purpose of this manual is to supplement the materials you encounter in courses in the psychology of adjustment, and especially the textbook by Spencer A. Rathus and Jeffrey S. Nevid, *Adjustment and Growth: The Challenges of Life*, Sixth Edition. Their textbook explains how the science of psychology investigates principles that help us meet the challenges of life, and this supplement asks us to experience these principles.

1

What Is Adjustment?

Name _____ **Date** _____

1.1 What Is Challenging?

Rathus and Nevid begin their first chapter with several examples of individuals facing challenges. They illustrate the nature of challenge for Beth, John, Maria, Lisa, and David, and they also review a litany of problems and opportunities that could serve as a checklist. Have you considered which ones apply to you? Some can be regarded as concerns, some as hassles, some as crises, and some as openings for growth. Try this: skip any issues that do not concern you, but count the number of issues in the list below that are (1) issues you have had to adjust to and are examples of your growth, and (2) issues that remain a challenge.

Interpersonal relations	Test taking
Family	Premarital living arrangements
Health	Career goals
Economics	Child care
Career	Life goals conflicts
Self-worth	Grades
School	Moral decisions
Environmental pollution	Food and eating
Sex	Insomnia
Politics	Motivation
Ethics	Depression
Emotions	Suicide
Concern for others	Role conflicts
Constraints of time	Self-esteem
Sexual orientation	Changing technology
AIDS and/or safe-sex practices	Religion
Alcohol	Personal budget
Divorce	Aging
Exercise	Drug abuse
Heart disease	Marriage
Cigarette smoking	Values
Job interviews	Studying
Tranquilizer use	Family planning
Social approval	Mental health
Gender issues in the workplace	Cultural diversity

How many issues fit category (1)? _16_ How many issues fit category (2)? _12_

Pat yourself on the back for each issue you have faced and managed. For those issues you still must face, consider the following possibility. Look in the index of your textbook and see if the book promises to discuss issues relevant to you. You may wish to look ahead, or even to visit the library or bookstore for references to supplement your reading.

It might be valuable to ask your classmates how many issues they recorded in each case. Everyone could submit their results anonymously, so it could be made apparent that everyone has some challenge to face. That might help your instructor to recognize which directions to take a class.

Follow-Up Questions:

1.   How many of the above issues were **not** faced by your parents?

2.   How many of the above issues were **not** faced by people 100 years ago?

3.   Have times become tougher?

4.   What classes on your campus address any of these challenges?

Name _____ Date _____

1.2   A Learning Theory Assessment of Your Studying

Learning theorists encourage us to analyze how reinforcers and punishments affect our behavior, and Chapter One recommends we use self-rewards for encouraging studying. It might be useful to attempt a "behavioral assessment" of studying behavior by asking ourselves these questions and recording our answers:

1.   What are my rewards for studying and how powerful are they?

2.   How soon after studying do I receive these rewards?

3.   What behaviors do I do instead of studying (to avoid it)?

4.   What are my rewards for these incompatible behaviors?

5.   How soon do the incompatible behaviors get rewarded?

6.   Which comes first, studying or other behaviors?

Now consider these general principles from learning theories:

1. Rewards are more effective when they are immediate.

2. Bigger rewards are more effective and weak rewards are less effective.

3. If we engage in less rewarding behavior before a more rewarding behavior, we may grow to like the less rewarding behavior and do it more and more.

In other words, if our main rewards for studying are grades, graduation, and maybe the approval of others, all of which are delayed, we can choose to follow studying with entertainment or socializing which are immediate and attractive rewards. Now if you will create a simple plan for organizing activities that can serve as immediate rewards for studying, you will have taken your first step as a behavioral technician. Write your plan here:

6

1.3   Research: A Way of Knowing

Chapter 1 explains the value of the scientific approach, and especially the role of research. Being able to do research can put you on the leading edge of knowledge, which is a valuable position in our "information age," whether your career takes you into business, human services, science, or industry.

To explore research as a tool for knowledge, follow the outline for research in Chapter 1, and pick one of the issues mentioned in the chapter.

1.   First, what is the nature of the problem?

2.   Formulate a research question.

3.   Form a hypothesis.

4.   How can you test your hypothesis?

5.   Imagine the hypothesis is supported, what can you conclude?

Name _____ Date _____

1.4　Planning Your Study Time

Taking an active rather than passive approach to studying can begin with the mastery of the material in your textbook. To organize your study plans, use a chart such as the one below to fill in the planned amount of study time and the planned number of pages to read at the beginning of the week. Fill in the actual amount of study time and the actual number of pages read each day. At the end of the week, compare the totals from the "planned" columns and the "actual" columns.

Adjust next week's plans according to how much leftover and new material remain to be studied. Each day that your "actual" total is equal to or greater than your "planned" column, you have met your study goals for that day and are entitled to reward yourself.

	Planned Amount of Study Time	Planned Number of Pages Read	Actual Study Time	Actual Number of Pages Read
Monday				
Tuesday				
Wednesday				
Thursday				
Friday				
Saturday				
Sunday				

8

2

Understanding People:
What Is Human Nature?

2.1   What Is Your Theory of Human Nature?

In the second chapter, Rathus and Nevid describe some of the most important theories of personality developed in this century by psychologists. We all have our own theories of human nature, whether they are explicit or implicit. Just as the people who construct such theories for a living, we tend to begin with observations and then hypotheses. What theories are we working with? Explore this by simply asking yourself if you think humans are more inclined to be kind and benevolent or more inclined to be egotistical, selfish, and only interested in "number one." To provoke some thinking here, decide which description of people you think is more accurate.

Sigmund Freud said:

"...men are not gentle friendly creatures wishing for love, who simply defend themselves if they are attacked, but...a powerful measure of desire for aggressiveness has to be reckoned with as part of their instinctual endowment. The result is that their neighbor is to them not only a helper or sexual object, but also a temptation to them to gratify their aggressiveness...to seize his possessions, to humiliate him, to cause him pain, to torture and to kill him...Anyone who calls to mind the atrocities of the early migrations of the invasions of the Huns or by the so-called Mongols under Ghengis Khan and Tamurlane, of the sack of Jerusalem by the pious crusaders, and even the horrors of the last world war, will have to bow his head humbly before the truth of this view of man...We see man as a savage beast to whom the thought of sparing his own kind is alien" (*Civilization and Its Discontents*, 1930).

Carl Rogers wrote:

"I have little sympathy with the rather prevalent concept that man is basically irrational, and that his impulses, if not controlled, will lead to destruction of others and self. Man's behavior is exquisitely rational, moving with subtle and ordered complexity toward the goals his organism is endeavoring to achieve" (*Journal of Consulting Psychology*, 1957).

Follow-Up Questions:

1.   Which position do you think is more accurate? Why?

11

2.   Since Freud cited historical cases to support his view, what examples could be used to refute him?

3.   Do either of the arguments above use case histories, correlated observations, or research findings to support the theories?

4.   What might be the best way to resolve this debate?

5.   What would the consequences be should the followers of each theorist, Freud and Rogers, be placed in charge of education? What if each point of view were represented by presidential candidates? Where else in society might big differences be created by the applications of these different models?

Name _____ Date _____

2.2   Researching Human Nature

We have been much encouraged to think that research is an important and powerful tool for answering questions about ourselves and others. If we use case histories to support one side or the other, it seems it will become a draw. There are lots of nice people in the world and lots of dangerous people. A tougher test of theories is to create hypotheses and to test them.

What hypotheses could address such basic issues as those raised by Freud and Rogers? Consider the following possibility as we engage in each of the four basic steps to the scientific method:

1.   Formulate a research question. When people are given a chance to be helpful, are they as ruthless as Freud says, or as benevolent as Rogers pictures? What do you think?

2.   Developing a hypothesis. When people find a wallet with identification and money in it, they are in a position to be helpful. What hypothesis would Freud and Rogers likely create to predict if we were purposely to drop wallets at various locations around campus? Also, what is your prediction? Express your predictions as percentages of wallets returned intact with money and identification inside.

3.   Testing a hypothesis. Where will you place or drop the wallets? How much money would you place in each, or would you choose different amounts? How will finders be able to return wallets if they choose to do so, and can they be returned anonymously?

13

4. <u>Drawing conclusions about the hypothesis</u>. Since this is speculation, unless you have vast resources upon which to draw, just imagine the outcomes fit your own predictions even better than Freud's and/or Rogers'. What could you conclude about the alternative theories? What other hypotheses and tests could you now create?

14

Name _____ Date _____

2.3   Creating Classical Conditioning

It is useful to start this activity by reading about Pavlov's work on classical conditioning, described in Chapter 2. He used dogs in his research, but we can use roommates and friends to explore classical conditioning. Simply ask a friend to hold out his or her hands with the palms turned up. Tell your subject to resist the moderate pressure you exert downward on his or her hands with your own hands. Each time, before you push down, say the word "Now!" then immediately press down. Repeat this four times. On the fifth occasion, sharply say "Now!" without pressing down. Did the hands rise up to meet yours? (If not, pronounce your friend less than a dog, and try another.) Now tell your subject that you will continue to place your hands just above his or hers and sharply say "Now!" until they no longer respond by raising their hands upward. Note how many trials until you "extinguish" his or her hand response. Finally, ask your friend to explain what happened and to write down what he or she tells you.

Follow-Up Questions:

1.   Using the above activity and your textbook, identify the:

   a.   Conditioned stimulus: _____

   b.   Unconditioned stimulus: _____

   c.   Conditioned response: _____

   d.   Unconditioned response: _____

2.   If the hand response extinguishes immediately after telling them not to respond to the stimulus "Now!", how would you explain the extinction? However, if it takes more than one trial to extinguish the response, what explanation would you use?

15

3.   What results did your classmates get?

4.   How did your subject explain what happened? Is it a behavioral explanation or a cognitive social explanation, phenomenological, or psychodynamic?

5.   What theory is best supported by your results?

3

Social Perception: How We See Others and Ourselves

Name _____ Date _____

3.1   Testing Our Perceptions

If there is a consistency in the theories of Freud, Erikson, Rogers, and Maslow, it may be the idea that adjustment depends on the accuracy of the perception of reality. It would seem that accurate perception would increase the likelihood of correct choices, reduce or eliminate anxieties from unnecessary worry, provide feedback for change, and so on and so on. In Chapter 3, Rathus and Nevid portray the virtues of accurate social perception. Only if we could see others more accurately without prejudice! Only if others could see us the same way!

Select a classmate, or roommate, for this activity which tests your perceptiveness. It will be a tough test so be prepared to encounter your limitations.

Ask a friend to recall or answer as well as possible and write down:

1.   The last two magazines read and circle the one they liked best.

2.   The last two movies seen and circle the one they liked best.

3.   Two television shows watched regularly and the one they prefer.

4.   Would they quit school or work if they won a $5,000,000 lottery?

5.   Would they sacrifice their life to save anyone in the world?

6.   Did they vote in the last election?

7.   Would they choose the sex of their first child?

You can make up and ask many more such questions. Now tell your subject what you think his or her answer will be on the first question and your rationale for it. Proceed through all the questions to test your accuracy. Maybe you would be willing to let your friend try the same thing with you as a target.

Follow-Up Questions:

1.   Are there any bases for predicting people's responses in advance?

2.   What leads you to correct predictions?

3.   What leads you to incorrect predictions?

3.2   Perceiving How Others Dress to Impress

Does your school require you to wear a uniform? Probably not, but it may be possible for students to choose some rather uniform ways to dress, which may be their attempt to make a statement about what they want us to think about them. Would you say that people use their clothing, hairstyles, and even facial expressions to help themselves achieve an identity?

This activity asks you to sit in the student union or another suitable location and catalog the different social identities you perceive others are trying to project. You might categorize some as Greek, some as Athletes, some as Art students, and so on. List your proposed labels here:

Follow-Up Questions:

1.   Can you do this without being negative? For example, are any of the labels you use derogatory, such as "nerds," "frat rats," or "animals"?

2.   Beside each label write the degree of confidence you have in assigning people you see in this category as a percentage from 0 to 100 percent. Does this idea alter the way you see this task?

3.   With classmates, create a single list of labels that will be useful for the next project. Assign a number to each label as a code. How many labels have you created?

Name _____ Date _____

Testing the Accuracy of Social Perceptions

Which labels in the list created for the last activity would you assign to yourself and your classmates? Can you correctly guess each others' assignments? Students have often found this activity to be one of the most revealing and interesting activities in this course.

1.   Each person has access to the master list created in Activity 3.2, which might be on the blackboard or another handy place.

2.   Assign a label to yourself from the list created by the class. Do not tell others what label you have chosen.

3.   Each person then prepares two response sheets. On the first sheet write down the names of everyone in the class and beside each name assign a stereotype from the master list you think best fits them. On the second sheet, write only your name.

4.   Pass the second sheet around the room systematically so each person can record the label or stereotype they chose for the named individual in question 3. When everyone has responded, each paper is returned to the person named at the top of the page.

5.   Students then reveal the label they originally chose to describe themselves. They can then check the accuracy of their label assignments against other students' perceptions of themselves.

Follow-Up Questions:

1.   Do people perceive you the way you thought they would?

2.   How accurate were your perceptions? What percentage of your labels did your classmates assign themselves?

3.   Look again in your textbook at the discussion regarding how to cope with prejudice and discrimination. Is it possible that this activity could alter the way we discriminate?

4

Social Influence: Being Influenced By— and Influencing—Others

Name _____ Date _____

4.1   Who's Listening?

"No one has ever lost money by underestimating the intelligence of the American people."

P. T. Barnum

We are confident that Mr. Barnum didn't have us in mind when he was estimating people's gullibility. But researchers repeatedly question how mindfully we handle attempts to influence us. Consider what you would predict people would do in response to these experimental conditions set forth by Harvard's Ellen Langer and her research group.

Imagine you have positioned yourself at a library table very near the photocopy machine. Each time someone starts to use the machine and before he or she puts money in it, you approach with one of three requests to use the machine without waiting. Estimate what percent of people will comply with each type of request:

1.   "Excuse me, I have five pages. May I use the Xerox machine?"

        Compliance estimate = _____ %

2.   "Excuse me, I have five pages. May I use the Xerox machine because I have to make copies?"

        Compliance estimate = _____ %

3.   "Excuse me, I have five pages. May I use the Xerox machine, because I am in a rush?"

        Compliance estimate = _____ %

Follow-Up Questions:

1.   What reasons would you give for any differences in your predictions?

2.   What real value is there in the reason given for request number 2?

3.   Now try to explain the results Langer reported for approaches 1, 2, and 3 respectively:
      60, 93, and 94 percent.

4.   What do Langer's results say about people's attempts to organize incoming information?

5.   The researchers also tested the same requests except they changed the number of pages
      from 5 to 20. These requests resulted in compliance rates of 24, 24, and 42 percent. How do
      you explain the differences from the first set of results, including a general decline in
      compliance, and the similar results for approaches 1 and 2? Langer has used the concepts
      "mindlessness" and "mindfulness" to account for these outcome differences. How do you
      think she used them?

26

Name _____ Date _____

4.2   A Simple Question

Compared to Britain and other nations, people in the U.S.A. watch more TV and, on the average, sets are switched on for seven hours a day. This would expose some of us to a considerable amount of effort to influence us through advertising.

For this activity, please watch your favorite commercial TV show this week. (Sorry about the hard assignment, but it will be a good lesson.) While watching, use a watch, clock, or calendar to keep track of the total time devoted to advertising and take some notes on your favorite ad. If you are not quite fast enough to catch it all, you might watch for the ad again. It is bound to be repeated, especially if it is interesting and well done. You will be able to identify some of the strategies used in the ad to persuade the audience by analyzing the characteristics of the communicator, the central and peripheral routes of the message, and the audience.

1. Is the communicator an expert, attractive, familiar, or similar to the intended listener? Why do you think he or she was chosen?

2. It is not uncommon for people strong in some of these qualities to be weak in others, and yet still be chosen. For example, ex-athletes often represent brands of beer, and actresses explain why it is good to buffer aspirin. Are they experts?

3. Would the use of music, dance, song, beautiful people or scenery (all known as production values) take advantage of the central or the peripheral route of influencing discussed in Chapter 4? What route was used in the ad you have chosen to analyze?

4.   What information used the central route?

5.   What audience do you think this ad is aimed at? Can you characterize the intended audience as to age, gender, and motivation to be mindful?

6.   Would you evaluate the ad as successful or not? Why or why not?

7.   In general, which influences you more? The communicator, the central message, or the peripheral messages?

Name _____ Date _____

4.3   What Would You Predict?

1.   Consider for a moment the next presidential election. What would influence you to become highly involved in the campaign of your choice for president? List your ideas here:

2.   Now suppose you want to persuade someone who does not know who they want to support to help you with the very big job of handing out leaflets for your candidate in public places on campus and elsewhere. Which techniques in the chapter can you use to influence this person to help?

3.   Predict your helper's attitude toward your favorite candidate if:

    a.   you only thank the helper for the help he or she gave you

    b.   you pay more than the usual amount students can earn in such jobs

4.4 Will We Be Willing to Help?

We are disturbed by the Kitty Genovese story, and probably ask ourselves what we would do in similar situations. After the discussions of helping behavior in Chapter 4, we realize that circumstances and even our mood may influence our willingness to help or remain a bystander. If we chose to be more helpful, we can consider ideas already discussed earlier in your textbook, and organize our thoughts to increase helping. Consider your answer to these questions:

1. How do you create a schema of yourself as a helper? What would be your ideal?

2. How do you practice being helpful? What are some common opportunities to use?

3. Is your assertiveness score on the Rathus Assertiveness Schedule high enough that you are comfortable that you can assert yourself when the occasion warrants it?

4. Social psychologists, who have led the work on helping research, are prone to investigate the situational variables that affect behavior—that's why it's called social psychology. While they may not emphasize enduring traits of persons as factors, we can speculate what traits might be worth investigating. What do you think would be worth studying?

Name _____ Date _____

4.5   Are Our Attitudes Being Manipulated by Madison Avenue?

It appears to me to be a very clever advertising campaign when I see a beer pegged as the choice of real mountain men. The ads are replete with implied similes about appreciating the "wildlife," and carrying six-packs instead of six-shooters. Of course we could not have expected advertisers to be so truthful as to include the possibilities of beer bellies and hangovers. Instead we are exposed to promises that the good life is a function of our beverage choice, with popularity and sex as bonuses if we choose wisely. To begin questioning the possible influence advertising could have we might start with our own experience.

1.   During this week, keep a diary of all alcohol and tobacco ads you encounter. Record the products and the total number of ads. You are likely to encounter ads in newspapers, television, radio, billboards, and points of purchase in stores. Would you include T-shirts, sponsorship of sports or music events, and insignias on equipment as ads also?

2.   Also record some information about the actors and models in the ads with particular attention to such details as their age, gender, appearance, and behavior. Other information includes to whom the ads are addressed, what implicit rewards are promised for using the product, and what kinds of behavior are encouraged by the ads.

31

5

Stress: Sources and Moderators

Name _____ Date _____

5.1   Sources of Stress: Hassles

In Chapter 5, we learned that stress can be associated with emotional distress, physical illness, poorer performance, and behavioral problems. Among the several sources of stress are the big changes in life, like graduation or marriage, and the daily hassles like broken shoestrings and snarled traffic. The Social Readjustment Rating Scale in Chapter 5 has us consider some of the major life changes that increase health risks and are associated with stress. In addition to your score on this scale, consider the possible effects of daily hassles by keeping a "hassles diary" for one week.

Follow-Up Questions:

1.   Which hassles occur at a frequent rate such as daily or several times daily?

2.   For each hassle identified, decide what would be best changed: 1) the hassle or
2) your response. For example, a more scenic route might eliminate the hassle of a difficult commute, while a problem with rainy weather might require a "change in attitude," or more precisely, challenging an irrational idea.

5.2   Where Can You Find "Merry Heart Medicine"?

When Norman Cousins tried to take some control over his own painful medical condition, he asked friends to bring funny films and videos to the hospital. His choices included Laurel and Hardy and Candid Camera. Where would you turn if you wanted to select humorous material?

Follow-Up Questions:

1.   If you wanted evidence that your humorous material was having a "medicinal" effect, what dependent variable could measure any benefits?

2.   What kind of humorous program could you envision for a pediatric ward at a local hospital?

5.3   A Moderator of Stress: Hardiness

Sources of stress do not automatically cause stress related problems. Moderators of stress which can include our personal strengths, might mean that we can have a healthier and more productive life in spite of life's challenges, or maybe even because of them. As your textbook mentions, Suzanne Kobasa and others have studied people who have successfully handled much stress without becoming ill. Kobasa and others have listed some of the strengths for moderating stress, which have been paraphrased below to illustrate the concept of hardiness, and to give us a chance to evaluate ourselves. For each strength, write one change that you could **realistically** make for personal improvement.

1.   Having a clear sense of goals, values, capabilities, and their importance.

2.   Active involvement to promote change.

3.   Finding personal meaning in stressful life events.

4.   Having a sense of control.

5.   Having a good support system.

6.   Seeking stimulation.

7.   Having a stable and even disposition.

8.   Having a Type B personality.

Critical Thinking:

Could any of the characteristics of hardy people be **results** of health, rather than **causes** of health? Select one characteristic and describe how it might be a result rather than a cause.

5.4 · **Why Do Married Men Live Longer Than Single Men?**

Some of the studies mentioned in your textbook, which support the relationship between social support and health, are correlational. Consider the observation that married men live longer than single men. What alternative explanations can you offer to the explanation that social support is the **cause** of longer living?

You might begin by thinking of what else is often different about being married and not being married.

Follow-Up Questions:

1. How could you test the alternative you generated?

2. Could men who prefer to remain bachelors gain the benefits of longevity and/or health that married men enjoy?

3. What is the effect of marriage for women?

39

6

Psychological Factors
and Physical Health

Name _____ Date _____

6.1　How Much Do We Value Health?

Ask yourself and as many others as you care to, the following questions to obtain some idea of our values about health. Before you finish, consider what additional questions you could ask?

1.　If you could achieve your ideal in only one of the following respects, while only achieving mediocrity in the others, which would you choose?

　　　　a.　Perfect health
　　　　b.　Perfect psychological well-being
　　　　c.　Perfect financial success
　　　　d.　Perfect career success
　　　　e.　Perfect spiritual success

2.　If a new drug were to be made legally available that increased happiness by ten percent, but reduced the length of life, how many years would you be willing to forfeit to use the drug? What if the drug were illegal?

3.　If you could sell years of your life to people willing to buy them, how many would you sell and for how much money?

4.　What is the most difficult health habit for you to acquire?

Name _____ Date _____

6.2   Demonstrating the Stress/Health Relationship

If you want to examine the effects of stress on health, you could ask people to record their physical ailments long before and shortly before a stressor such as final examinations. To actually do so would require that you investigate your school's human research guidelines and follow them to protect the rights and well-being of the subjects. Even if you do not attempt any actual data collection, you can design a research proposal. You will have to decide such issues as how many subjects, how health complaints can be recorded, which times recording takes place, and if possible how control subjects can be used to help verify any effects of stress.

1.   Where can you recruit subjects and how many do you believe you will need?

2.   How can your subjects' physical complaints be assessed?

3.   When can you test the subjects to illustrate any effects of stress?

4.   What kinds of differences, and how much in the way of differences, are necessary to verify stress effects?

Name _____ Date _____

6.3   The Physiology of Stress

As we learn about the autonomic nervous system and its role in our response to stress, we can create a demonstration of the response of two involuntary reactions, one in our heart rate, and one in our rate of perspiration. Changes in heart rate and perspiration are two of the physiological changes observed in stress research and also in so-called "lie detection" testing. If you can do these with a friend or classmate, you will be able to create a "balance order" of effects.

1.   Alone, or together, take your resting heart rate and record the number of beats for one minute (BPM).

   Your BPM   Friend's BPM

   _____   _____

2.   To create a mild, temporary stressor, cough hard three times in a row. Your partner, if included, can skip the coughing this time for comparison.

   Your 2nd BPM   Friend's 2nd BPM

   _____   _____

3.   If applicable, change roles with your friend, and let them cough hard three times in a row while you relax. Then immediately count the heart rates after they cough.

   Your 3rd BPM   Friend's 3rd BPM

   _____   _____

4.   After your heart rate(s) return to their original level, both of you cough hard three times and count BPMs until they recover to within two beats of the original level. How long does it take to recover?

   Minutes for you   Minutes for your friend

   _____   _____

45

5. You can create a similar demonstration showing the response of the skin to a stressor. In bright light, or outside on a sunny day, look at the pad of your index finger. As you turn or tilt your finger, you will probably see it sparkle from the oils and sweat on it. These can be seen even better with slight magnification. If you wipe the finger on a cloth, the sparkle will be removed. How long does it take to return to this sparkling state if you cough as above? How long does it take if you just wait?

Follow-Up Questions:

1. Who responds stronger to the coughing?

2. How could you measure the recovery from the coughing?

3. What branch of the autonomic nervous system have you just witnessed?

4. According to your textbook, what other physical changes took place in response to the coughing and how could they be measured?

5. What stage or stages of the General Adaptation Syndrome have you demonstrated?

7

Issues in Personal Health: Nutrition, Exercise, Sleep, and Drugs

7.1   Personal Attitudes Toward Some Health-Related Issues

While considering the health-related problems below, which do you think would be the most difficult to experience? What would be next, and so forth? Rank from 1 to 5, the worst to the least troubling:

1. Addiction to alcohol   _____

2. Addiction to cocaine   _____

3. Obesity   _____

4. Insomnia   _____

5. Heart disease   _____

Follow-Up Questions:

1. Considering these problems, which one is the object of the most ridicule? What defense could be offered for bashing these people?

2. Which of the problems do you think is the most difficult to correct? Why?

3.   When and how much alcohol is safe to drink?

4.   How much do you weigh, and what is your ideal weight?

5.   How much sleep is ideal and how much do you prefer?

You will learn a great deal about health and health-related issues in this chapter. When you finish, you may find that you need to reconsider some of your answers. As always, you could ask others to reconsider their ideas about the above questions.

7.2   New Weight Guidelines

We can often turn to the government and other institutions for good information about nutrition, weight, and health. It might be interesting to compare your ideal weight from question 4 in Activity 7.1 with a fairly new set of tables for healthy weight from the U. S. Department of Agriculture and Health and Human Services. In comparison to previous tables and guidelines, these are more forgiving and allow a wider range of weights at each height. The source is the *1990 Dietary Guidelines for Americans.*

Height	Weight (lbs.)	
	19 to 34 years	35 years and over
5'0"	97-128	108-138
5'1"	101-132	111-143
5'2"	104-137	115-148
5'3"	107-141	119-152
5'4"	111-146	122-157
5'5"	114-150	126-162
5'6"	118-155	130-167
5'7"	121-160	134-172
5'8"	125-164	138-178
5'9"	129-169	142-183
5'10"	132-174	146-188
5'11"	136-179	151-194
6'0"	140-184	155-190
6'1"	144-189	159-205
6'2"	148-195	164-210

51

Name _____ **Date** _____

7.3   Testing Our Aerobic Fitness

Your textbook offers many reasons to exercise and quite a few guidelines for beginning and maintaining an aerobic training program. You might find the following test a challenging and rewarding way to chart your progress. Please observe the standard health precautions discussed in Chapter 7 before attempting this test if you are not already exercising, are a smoker, have a family history of heart disease, are overweight, or are over 40. Time yourself and perhaps a friend or date if you care to, for a one and one-half mile run/walk. Your aerobic fitness rating can then be compared to the standards in the chart below (for all ages 13 and over).

Aerobic Fitness of Males and Females Estimated from 1.5 Mile Run*

	High (in minutes)	Low (in minutes)	Average (in minutes)
Males	9:29	12:39	11:29
Females	13:38	18:50	16:57
Sailing Team	9:54	11:49	10:43

*Source: Sharkey (no date)

You can use the 1.5 mile run to assess your status and your progress. You could also choose to repeat and time almost any similar task to measure progress. You do not have to compare yourself to any other people or a set of arbitrary standards to be motivated.

Name _____ Date _____

7.4   Sleep: The Gentle Tyrant or Benign Dictator?

Samuel Johnson called sleep the gentle tyrant because we cannot resist it, but we could also call sleep a benign dictator because it serves the body and mind as a clock that helps to organize the hundreds of functions that cycle through the 24-hour period. Sleep is only one of the clocks for controlling patterns that influence almost everything about us including our moods, our intelligence, and most bodily functions. Without these clocks, we might experience permanent jet lag. They seem to interact and help each other organize so we are generally at our best during the day.

One of the other clocks for controlling our body and mind is our core temperature, which is higher during our wake time and lower when we sleep. Even if we stay up all night, our temperatures still drop to their lowest levels at night and begin rising as our normal wake up time approaches. Those functions that use core temperature for their timing go on as normal. Not so those functions that use sleep as a timer for control. Such desynchronization is largely responsible for discomfort and poor performance following a sleepless night. Usually, one or two nights of sleep restores synchronization, and we feel better.

Occasionally specialists are asked to help people who have slept so poorly or inconsistently that their patterns and body clocks are confused. We often rely on oral temperature records to let us know where these people stand. Typically, if we take our temperature with an oral thermometer first thing int he morning,it will be several tenths of a degree cooler than just a few hours later. Then, in the late evening, as the day wanes, the pattern reverses and our temperature drops as our sleep time approaches. Sleep medicine specialists can use this pattern to study jet lag, depression, and other problems that seem to be highly related to the coordination of the patterns. For example, many depressed people show little or no pattern of core temperature changes.

You may find it interesting to graph your oral temperatures over the course of several days to verify this pattern, and also to see if it tends to correlate with your tendencies to be a morning person, otherwise known as a "Lark," or an evening person, known as an "Owl," or something in between (see Activity 7.5). Morning temperatures tend to rise faster for Larks and more slowly for Owls. Knowing our own pattern can help us choose class times or design our own schedules.

With an oral thermometer, sample your temperature several times each day for one week. Plot the temperatures on the following graph. Estimate the curving lines that run through the points, and best fits your data. You will find a prepared graph on the back of this page.

Daily Oral Temperatures

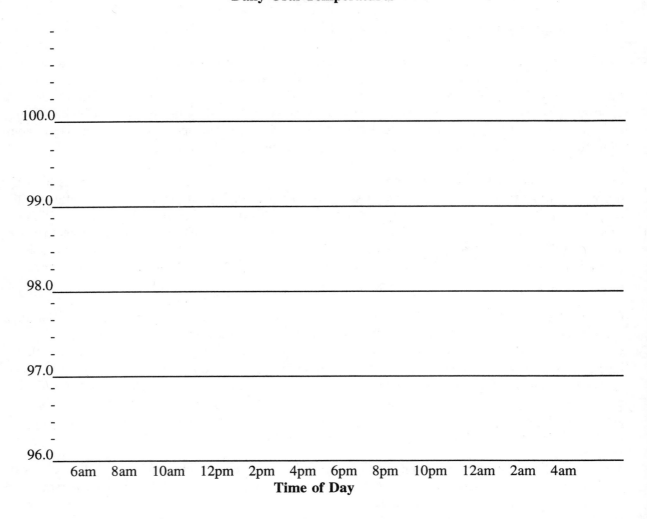

Name _____ Date _____

7.5   Are You a "Lark" or an "Owl"?

Some of us hit the floor running when we get up in the morning. We usually eat breakfast, prefer morning classes, and do not care to stay up "past our bedtime" without some very good reason. This is the pattern of "Larks," or morning people. Others of us hate getting up in the morning, avoid breakfast, and do not need an excuse to stay up late, even to watch a television show that has little attraction. This is the pattern of "Owls," or evening people. Still more of us fit neither extreme case, and fall somewhere in between. Use the questions below to create a better idea of your patterns.

1.   Estimate the number of breakfasts you skip each week (0-7):

2.   Estimate how often you "sleep in" each week (0-7):

3.   Estimate how often you stay up past your best sleep time each week (0-7):

4.   Estimate what time you feel and respond your very best (am/pm):

Total the scores on items 1-3: Total = _____

The higher your score, the more you are like an "Owl" in your waking/sleeping pattern. Conversely, the lower your score, the more you are like a "Lark."

7.6   Taming the Tyrant

Even gentle tyrants are at times unable to get their way, and so many people suffer a range of sleep-related difficulties. In addition to insomnia, as discussed in Chapter 7, some people sleep too long, some suffer from pattern disruption caused by shift work, and some people even create their own difficulties by keeping irregular sleep schedules. If we want to feel our best during the day and sleep better at night, we are told that it is best to maintain regular sleep patterns. To assess the regularity of your sleep, or lack of it, keep the following simple diary. You may want to do this activity at the same time you keep track of your daily oral temperature (Activity 7.4).

Date	Wake Time	Sleep Start Time

Follow-Up Questions:

1.   How much do you vary your sleep start? Various studies indicate that more than two hours' variation can have detrimental effects on daytime performance.

2.   Do you sleep in after late nights? Research suggests that this will also decrease daytime abilities.

3.   Did you experience any "Sunday night insomnia"? If we stay up later on weekends, we may delay our biological clocks and create problems, possibly including "Monday blues." It is best to keep to our regular patterns as much as possible by waking at our usual times even when we stay up late. While there is little trouble if we lose some sleep, there can be a problem if we disrupt our schedules.

7.7   Questioning Ourselves

1.   Two Seattle cocktail waiters were fired because they did not want to serve a strawberry daiquiri to a pregnant woman (*Newsweek*, 1991). It raises an issue that could quickly divide opinions. Would you favor laws that would prevent or restrict pregnant women from smoking, drinking alcohol, or abusing drugs? What would be your most important argument for such laws? On the other hand, what would be the most powerful argument against such laws?

For:

Against:

2.   If you were throwing a party, would you serve alcohol to a pregnant woman? Justify your response.

3.   If drugs were to become available that could improve life in some ways but cause life to be shorter, what choices would you make regarding your use of such drugs? How many years of your life, if any, would you give up to experience a 25 percent improvement in:

   a.   Intelligence   _____years

   b.   Attractiveness   _____years

   c.   Physical strength   _____years

   d.   Sexual enjoyment   _____years

   e.   Popularity   _____years

4. When do you say when? How many alcoholic beverages at the **most** would you want to see the following people consume in one evening?

    a.   Your date   _____

    b.   Your designated driver   _____

    c.   Your best friend   _____

    d.   Your minister   _____

    e.   Your parent(s)   _____

    f.   Yourself   _____

5. Except for the designated driver, who should not drink any alcohol? How do you explain any differences in your answers? Are any sexist attitudes or stereotypes influencing your judgments?

6. What answers do other people give to these questions?

58

Name _____ **Date** _____

7.8   Social Approval of Alcohol Abuse

At some point in our lives we decide what our approach to alcohol should be. One influence we can document is peer pressure. If friends and roommates frequently voice approval of "getting wasted," "getting bombed," or "getting ripped," it would be hard to avoid the conclusion that alcohol should be used as a drug, rather than a beverage. Try this activity for one week:

1.   How many times does someone speak of intoxication as if it is desirable or acceptable, and how often is it spoken of in disapproving ways?

2.   What words or phrases are used as synonyms for intoxication?

3.   How many times did you catch yourself speaking of alcohol the same way?

4.   Where do you draw the line between use and abuse of alcohol?

Name _____ Date _____

7.9   Does Smoking and Secondary Smoke Affect Heart Rate?

People who are allergic to or bothered by secondary cigarette smoke may not want to participate in this activity except at a distance. If you smoke or know someone who smokes, you may be able to see one of the physiological affects of nicotine first hand. You would want to be tactful in requesting the cooperation of someone so the request is not interpreted as a challenge.

1.   Take a base rate of the smoker's heart rate after a typical amount of time has passed since the last cigarette—at least an hour or so. The pulse can be monitored at the wrist or neck for one minute.

Record here _____

2.   Now if you intend to remain close enough to be affected by the secondary smoke of the smoker, take your own heart rate before asking them to light up.

Record your heart rate here _____

3.   Allow the smoker to smoke one cigarette and monitor the heart rate at the end of five minutes, even if he or she is still smoking.

Record the smoker's second heart rate here _____

4.   Record your second heart rate here _____

5.   What have you been able to demonstrate?

6.   Please explain your feelings about smokers' rights.

7.   Now you may wish to compare your notes with your classmates.

8

Psychological Disorders

8.1   What Is Abnormal?

When legal cases such as John Hinckley's and Billy Milligan's involve pleas of "not guilty by reason of insanity," it is common to read that the defense was able to find expert witnesses who testified the defendant was "insane," while the prosecution was also able to call expert witnesses who testified the defendant was "sane." Who is right? Much of the problem is created by the difficulty of defining insanity. The same problem occurs when we try to define abnormal. It is easy to recognize the extreme cases, but often difficult to decide the cases in between, which are the majority. Consider your textbook's criteria of psychological disorder and think of a case that satisfies the definition, yet would not be likely to be called abnormal. For example, wearing bow ties or beehive hair styles may be unusual, which is the first criterion, but will not cause a diagnosis of "psychological disorder."

1.   Identify an **unusual behavior** that is not an example of a psychological disorder.

2.   Identify an **unacceptable behavior** that is not an example of a psychological disorder.

3.   What **faulty perception of reality** is not an example of a psychological disorder?

4.   When might **severe personal distress** fail to be considered an example of a psychological disorder?

5.   Name a **self-defeating behavior** that would not be an example of a psychological disorder.

6. Name a behavior that is dangerous but not considered an example of a psychological disorder.

7. For a real challenge, identify a behavior that is all of the above, or as much of the above as possible, but is not regarded as a psychological disorder.

8. Now write an alternative definition of psychological disorder. (If you can manage this, you might become famous!)

9. Which model of psychological disorders would your definition best fit?

Name _____ Date _____

8.2   Checking Our Attitudes Toward People With Psychological Disorders

Suppose the government leased the apartments or home next door to your residence and converted them into use for the following people. Which types of handicaps or disorders, if any, would create the most discomfort for you? Rank each from 1 to 4, with 1 representing the most alarming, and 4 representing the least alarming.

_____ Mentally retarded

_____ Psychologically disordered

_____ Recovering alcoholics

_____ Returning convicted criminals

1.   What would be your worst fears in each case above?

   a.

   b.

   c.

   d.

2.   Ask others the same questions and record their responses here:

   a.

   b.

   c.

   d.

3.   Have you any evidence that prejudices exist against the people who are labeled psychologically disordered?

4.   What ill effects could prejudices cause the psychologically handicapped?

8.3   You Make the Diagnosis

Diagnosis is not always as easy as it looks, and diagnosticians can disagree about a label easily if certain features of a person's problems are more prominent at some times and not at other times, or if behaviors associated with one disorder can be associated with a different disorder as well. For instance, people can cry when they are sad, but people can also cry when they are happy. Take another look at the case of "Bonnie" in Chapter 8 and answer these questions:

1.   Which of her behaviors could lead to a diagnosis of **phobia**?

2.   Which of her behaviors could lead to a diagnosis of **depression**?

8.4   A Second Look at Bonnie's Case

Good diagnosticians want to look for a phenomenon known as **secondary gain**. Secondary gain occurs when the disorder results in rewards. An example in your textbook describes the inability to fly missions when some bomber pilots developed a type of conversion disorder including night blindness. You may remember that memory failures in dissociative disorders were linked to avoidance of painful thoughts, and thus can also illustrate secondary gain.

1.   Can you detect any possible secondary gain for Bonnie?

2.   In your opinion, is there any merit in hypothesizing that secondary gain plays any role in the problems Bonnie is experiencing?

3.   How could you test to see if secondary gain is involved or not?

4.   Is it necessary to assume that secondary gain is the only principle that is needed to explain Bonnie's difficulties?

8.5 Finding Help for Someone Considering Suicide

After reading the discussion of suicide, you probably found the suggestions for helping someone who is contemplating suicide quite valuable. In a real crisis it might be difficult to comply quickly with some of the recommendations including finding professional help. Answer these questions and you can be steps ahead in a real crisis.

1. What is the phone number of a "hotline" you can call?

2. How long did it take you to answer question number one? If you gathered the results for your class, the emergency service that administers the hotline might appreciate learning your results.

3. Does your school have a counseling center or any service that can respond to emergencies including potential suicide? Does this service have data on the frequency of emergency phone calls? Is it a 24-hour service?

9

Therapies: Ways of Helping

Name _____ Date _____

9.1   Asking Ourselves

After reading this chapter on therapies, you probably will have some opinions about psychotherapies. If you have not read the chapter yet, look at the first question and keep it in mind as you read.

1.   If you or someone you know were looking for a psychotherapist, which system or type of therapy would you choose or recommend and why?

2.   Now consult the yellow pages of your local phone directory under the two headings "psychologists" and "psychiatrists" (the latter are often listed under physicians). Which schools of psychotherapy are represented, and is your choice included?

3.   Without asking, write down how you believe your adjustment instructor would answer question number 1 above. Even if your instructor has no preference, he or she might be interested in knowing what kind of impression you have.

71

9.2   As Simple as ABC

Based on the discussion of Albert Ellis's Rational Emotive Therapy, try to interpret the following situation and offer some hypothetical assistance. A student-acquaintance informs you that he or she has failed an important exam in a required math class and is depressed and considers the situation in that class hopeless.

1.   What is "A," the activating event?

2.   What seems to be the "C," or consequences in this case?

3.   Which irrational belief(s), or "B", could be applicable in this example?

4.   What arguments would you propose to dispute these irrational beliefs?

5.   What was the last event that upset you?

6.   What feelings and thoughts did that event cause?

7.   Which irrational belief or beliefs could account for your responses?

8.   How would Albert Ellis challenge the ABC's in your example?

9.3   Constructing the Anxiety Item Hierarchy

To conduct systematic desensitization, clients help their therapists to arrange disturbing stimuli in an order of increasing challenge known as an anxiety item hierarchy. For this activity, choose a topic, behavior, or situation you associate with fear or anxiety. It does not need to be something that results in feelings of phobic proportions. For example, it could be competing in a race, telling the boss she or he made a mistake, looking over the edge of "Lover's Leap," or taking lessons in scuba. Some people find that the construction of the hierarchy alone can reduce some of their apprehension.

1.   Identify one item for a hierarchy that could be the first and least disturbing item. For example, related to the challenges discussed above, first items could be registering one week before the race, telling the boss the mail has arrived, standing 100 feet from the edge of Lover's Leap, or calling the scuba school to inquire about the cost of lessons.

2.   Now identify the most distressing situation you can imagine for the challenge you have chosen. Again, for example: a competitor says "you don't belong in the race," the boss yells "you're fired," you lean over the edge of the cliff, or you find no air coming to the mouthpiece.

3.   Now for your challenge, arrange, eight to eighteen stimuli in-between the two you have chosen, trying your best to make the perceived difference between each item about equal. If you have chosen a complex situation to cope with, it may take more than 20 items in your hierarchy, so don't hesitate to write more.

9.4   Identifying Caffeine Consumption

Among the self-control techniques outlined in this chapter is the functional analysis of behavior. By recording information about problem behaviors, including the stimuli that encourage the behavior, and the situation in which the behavior occurs, we may see change occur in reaction to functional analysis, or at least gain ideas about the steps that could lead to successful intervention. For our project we can focus on consumption of caffeine. Prepare a note card so you can record caffeine consumption including all caffeinated beverages and over-the-counter medications you use, the time, location, and rewards for use. Remember the colas, Dr. Pepper, Mountain Dew, chocolate, some analgesics, and some cold preparations are likely candidates for inclusion. You may find possible rewards include stimulation, socialization, prevention of headaches, or you may chalk it up to simple "habit." Can you record any adverse consequences you experience caused by caffeine, such as sleeplessness, nervousness, headaches, stomach complaints, and so on? What situations prompt you to use caffeine?

Follow-Up Questions:

1.   Is caffeine required to prevent an unpleasant effect such as headache or sleeplessness?

2.   What is the average number of doses of caffeine taken per day? How does this compare to numbers reported by classmates?

3.   What self-control strategies could help reduce your caffeine consumption based on your functional analysis?

74

10

Methods of Coping:
Ways We Help Ourselves

10.1   Challenging Irrational Thoughts

In the previous chapter we read about irrational beliefs, and we identified an occasion of some personal distress to analyze by applying Albert Ellis's ABC approach. The current chapter on ways of helping ourselves is described as a do-it-yourself chapter and asks us to take on some very valuable challenges. We can begin by practicing some of the recommendations with hypothetical cases before addressing our own situations. For each example of catastrophizing, write an incompatible and rational rebuttal, and/or an alternative as illustrated in Chapter 10.

1.   "If I flunk this test I'll just die!"

2.   "I'll feel stupid if the teacher calls on me today."

3.   "I'm too embarrassed to exercise in public."

4.   "My parents never gave me a chance to develop any self-esteem."

5.   "That @#%^&* driver had no right pulling out in front of me!"

6.   "There will never be another love like the one I just lost."

Name _____ Date _____

10.2   Controlling Our Own Disturbing Thoughts

We should be ready to take the steps recommended in Meichenbaum's three-step procedure. For this week, keep a diary of any occasions when you feel any discomfort including fear, anger, frustration, pessimism, anxiety, and so forth. For some of us, one day's experience could keep us busy writing for a week, but a full week is a better representation of our experience. Note cards or slips of paper will serve, as long as we record each step for each occurrence. We will not provide all the space you might need for a diary, but answer the following questions in the spaces below.

1.   How many events during this week were recorded as distressing?

2.   Choose six that appear to involve the use of unnecessary, catastrophizing thoughts. For each case, compose more appropriate thoughts as practiced in the above activity.

        a.

        b.

        c.

        d.

        e.

        f.

Name _____ Date _____

10.3   Monitoring Arousal and Relaxation

It is hard to imagine a more positive step we can take in gaining control of our lives than deciding to control stress by learning to lower arousal. Chapter 10 details two very effective and well-researched techniques—meditation and progressive relaxation. Monitoring the effects of these techniques can be interesting and rewarding. The easiest way to verify the arousal-lowering potential of meditation or progressive relaxation is to take one-minute heart rates before and after practice. However, not everyone will detect a change in heart rate. For some people, improvements from relaxation are experienced as slower breathing, less muscle tension, or blood chemistry changes. To see if your heart rate is indicative of changes in your level of arousal, take your pulse for one minute, then engage in one of the recommended techniques detailed in your textbook, and finish by taking your pulse again for one minute.

1.   Your resting pulse prior to meditation or relaxation:

_____

2.   Your pulse immediately after the chosen technique:

_____

3.   For comparison purposes, see how you respond to music. Record your heart's BPM before listening here:

_____

4.   What happens if you vary the musical choices between rowdy and relaxing?

5.   If possible, compare yourself with others in your class and record your observations:

10.4   Monitoring Progress in Lowering Arousal

You have read that lowering arousal is worthwhile and will lead to possible improvements in health and performance, so it would be rewarding to verify our progress as we practice meditation and relaxation over days and weeks. One thing that has worked well is to keep a simple arousal diary that records how strong muscle tension is when you first notice it and how strong it remains as you attempt to lower it. Make a note every time you become aware of muscle tension, such as hunching your shoulders during class, or clutching your steering wheel with white knuckles, or wrinkling your forehead while you study or work. Rank your tension on a 10-point scale with 10 equal to the most severe strain possible and 1 equal to a total lack of any tension. Next, try to relax as well as possible and judge the new level of muscle tension on the same 10-point scale. What is commonly reported is 1) to notice more and more unnecessary cases of muscle tension, and 2) to include less severe examples as you become more sensitive to signals about your level of arousal, and 3) to record improvement in the ability to reduce tension to lower levels. Keep a note card or slip of paper in your pocket, purse, or wallet so you can record the two numbers on each occasion. Keep the days separate and at the end of the week answer these questions:

1.   Record the total number of times you noticed tension each day.

2.   For each day, record the average level of tension which you first noticed.

3.   For each day, record the average amount of improvement when you tried to relax.

4.   At the end of the project, can you find any changes or improvement in:

   a.   Increased recognition of occasions of tension?

   b.   Greater sensitivity to even lower levels of unnecessary tension?

   c.   Greater reductions in tension after attempting to relax?

80

10.5   Handling Hostility and Frustration

In Chapter 10, your textbook summarizes the rational restructuring procedures described by Albert Ellis. Putting yourself in the shoes of other people and imagining the reasons they may have for their behavior can help you control hostility and frustration when their behavior interferes with your efforts to achieve your own goals. These procedures work! Try this activity to practice empathizing with others, in order to manage the ill feelings that are sometimes created by their actions.

1. Think of a reasonable justification another driver would possibly give you for pulling out in front of your car from a side street, in a way which would cause you to have to brake quickly to avoid hitting him or her.

2. Think of the reasonable justifications an instructor could have for asking students not to call his or her house the night before tests to confirm information about the assigned reading.

3. Consider the last time someone, who you were not able to talk to, did something that made you angry. For example, it might have been the way one of your least favorite politicians voted on a bill or measure. Now try to put yourself in their shoes to imagine the justification they would offer for the situation.

11

Gender Roles and Gender Differences

Name _____ Date _____

11.1   Riddles

These riddles have been around for quite awhile, but they may still be useful for our purposes.

1.   A man and his son are in a serious car accident. Both are rushed to the nearest hospital while unconscious. The boy needs emergency surgery, but the emergency room surgeon says, "I can't operate on him, he's my son." How is this possible?

2.   If you enjoy sports, you might get this one. How can two softball teams play a complete softball game, and the score ends 1 to nothing, even though not one man for either team has crossed home plate?

3.   I really doubt the riddles fooled you, given they are old and given the subject for this chapter. However, you may find they will work on a friend or acquaintance. Try them one at a time, separate them by a day or so, and see if your subject learns anything from the first to the second riddle, assuming you told him or her the answer to the first. What happens and what hypotheses might be generated from this information?

Name _____ Date _____

11.2   Reversal of Roles

It is not uncommon to read about or be entertained by people's real or imagined experience with role reversal. What kinds of answers do you come up with to the following questions?

1.   Movies I can think of that have featured the theme of role reversal include "Mr. Mom," "Mrs. Doubtfire," "Tootsie," "Three Men and a Baby," the "Alien" trilogy, and "Three Men and a Little Lady." What movies can you add to this list?

2.   Our nation's experience in the Persian Gulf War brought home the reality of women in combat missions. What limits, if any, would you recommend for women serving in the armed services when it comes to combat missions, and/or the draft?

3.   Ask someone else the same question found in 2 above. What is her or his opinion?

86

11.3   Dear Old Sexist School Days

In your textbook, Rathus and Nevid detail how gender roles are reinforced in the education system. Researchers have found that sex bias continues beyond primary and secondary education right into the lecture halls and laboratories of American universities and colleges. For example, a University of Illinois study found that while high school valedictorians, salutatorians, and honor students were attending the University of Illinois, self-concepts remained steady for males, but dropped dramatically for females. Upon graduating from high school, 23 percent of the males and 21 percent of the females rated themselves as "far above average" in intelligence. By the time they were seniors in college, the numbers for the males and females were respectively, 25 percent and zero.

Are college instructors biased in the ways research suggests, such as calling on male students more, making better eye contact with males, supporting male students more, and coaching males more? To assess such possibilities at your school, select one class other than this adjustment class, and record for one week the following information.

1.   Did the instructor favor one gender by disproportionately calling on, helping, encouraging, or agreeing with either the men or the women in that class? How can you accurately record this data? Can anyone else in the class you have chosen also record the same data, so you could check for agreement (which we call reliability)?

2.   In addition to your effort to carefully look at one selected class, where else in your school have you run into gender bias? I have been utterly astonished at the stories of blatant as well as less obvious sexism reported on college campuses. If you cannot think of any examples from your own experience, ask your friends if they have had such experiences. What have you learned?

3.   What hypotheses could you create to systematically test and document the effects of gender bias in higher education?

4.   What other explanations might account for the University of Illinois findings?

11.4   Thinking Makes It So

Shakespeare wrote: "Nothing is either good or bad, thinking makes it so." What may be meat for one person may be poison for another. It's in the eye of the beholder. And so forth and so forth. By the same token, we can substitute an attractive synonym for something much less attractive, or we can turn things around the other way and make something wonderful or grand sound ugly or base. Word games like these can be used to create or maintain sexual bias. For each of the words below, think of two synonyms that can be substituted for the word—one positive and one negative. For example, we can substitute both "rational" and "unfeeling" for "stable," or "childish" and "creative" for "spontaneous."

	POSITIVE	NEGATIVE
consistent	_____	_____
warm	_____	_____
generous	_____	_____
stubborn	_____	_____
self-righteous	_____	_____
different	_____	_____
ambitious	_____	_____
serious	_____	_____
jaded	_____	_____

Name _____ Date _____

11.5   Interviewing Others

Since we can learn so much from others, consider one or both of these possible interviews. One could be a child and the other an adult engaged in a career not typical for that person's gender, such as a male nurse, or a female firefighter.

1.   With parental permission, question a child about issues raised in this chapter about early appearance of gender-role stereotyping. What questions can you think of and what are the child's answers?

2.   Interview the adult with some questions prepared in advance, but also with flexibility to pursue some unanticipated but promising leads. What can you share from your conversations?

12

Interpersonal Attraction:
Of Friendship, Love, and Loneliness

12.1   What Kind of Face Could Launch a Thousand Ships?

As your textbook says, it may not seem intelligent and sophisticated, but physical appearance is given a lot of importance in interpersonal attraction. Homer claimed that it was the face of Helen of Troy that precipitated the Trojan Wars. Certainly the Greeks knew how to appreciate physical appearance, and they left a classical, idealized legacy for Western Civilization to admire, ponder, and replicate. They are often given credit for defining the ideal characteristics of faces still followed by plastic surgeons today. While most of us might not know much about art, or faces, we know what we like. However, before we examine this fascinating information, seriously try to draw an idealized face on the back of this page. Many of you may not have a clue as to how to begin, so here are some rules for shaping the face (at least basically).

1.   Construct a rectangle so that the height is approximately 25 percent taller than the width (for example, four inches wide by five inches tall). Now divide the height by two horizontal lines so the rectangle is divided into equal thirds (for example, one line 1 and 2/3 inches from the top, and one line 1 and 2/3 inches from the bottom of the original rectangle).

2.   Next divide the length of the rectangle into equal fifths. In our example, this requires four vertical lines spaced 0.80 inches apart from each other and the sides of the original rectangle.

3.   Now do what you do when you doodle, and doodle the ears between the middle horizontal lines.

4.   Place the nose in the middle section, neatly fitting on the bottom line and between the two sides.

5.   Place the eyebrows at the tops of the two sections to the sides of the nose section.

6.   Place the eyes under the eyebrows and fully between the side lines of this section.

7.   In the section immediately below the nose, place the lips 1/3 of the way down the section and fully extending to and slightly past the sides of the section.

8.   Now, find a magazine photo of the most attractive face and report how well the face conforms to the specifications above.

9.   Collect five photos of faces you find attractive, and identify any additional specifications for attractiveness that were omitted above. Believe me, there are many more.

12.2   Is Your Love Like a Red, Red Rose?

Clearly, the word "love" gets overused when it can be applied to the most important person in our life and broccoli. Rathus and Nevid recognize this and make some suggestions about a more exact language of love, especially the different styles of love. The discussion suggests most people in love experience a combination of several different styles.

Think about the "ideal" you have of love, and see if you can assign some percentage from 0 to 100 percent to each of the styles. Beside each style enter your ideal percentage.

1.   _____ Eros or romantic love

2.   _____ Ludus or game-playing love

3.   _____ Storge or friendship love

4.   _____ Pragma or pragmatic, logical love

5.   _____ Mania or possessive, excited love

6.   _____ Agape or selfless love

Follow-Up Questions:

1.   Would the relationship best be described as romantic love or companionate love as they are described in your textbook?

2.   Looking back on a relationship in your past which ended, what percentages would you have assigned in that case? Is there any lesson in that?

3.   If you are involved in a relationship, have your partner write down the percentages for his or her vision of ideal love. How does this compare with your ideal?

4.   Try comparing your ideal love with a relationship portrayed in a novel, on a television show, or in a movie. What percentages could you use to describe the couple's relationship?

5.   Think about an influential couple you knew while growing up—perhaps your parents, grandparents, or close family friends. What percentages would you assign to their love? Would you want a relationship like theirs?

Name _____ Date _____

12.3   Coffee Shop Observations

Next time you are in the student union, coffee shop, cafeteria, or any place where people sit at a table together, observe some of the nonverbal communication and answer these questions:

1.   What body language do people use to convey they are "in love" with the other person?

2.   What body mannerisms suggest to you that two people are not romantically interested in each other, even though they are talking?

3.   Looking at still another conversation, what can be deduced about the relationship being experienced by the two people at that table, and why?

12.4　Is Love Insane?

George Bernard Shaw is quoted as saying love is "the most violent, most insane, most delusive, and most transient of emotions."

1.　What arguments or examples from experience, could you use to **support** his characterization of love?

2.　What rebuttals could be used to **refute** his contentions?

13

Intimate Relationships and Communication: A Guide on How to Get from Here to There

13.1   Opening Lines

When it comes to winning friends and influencing people, many of us find it all to easy to identify with Allan Felix (from your textbook). When we notice someone who is appealing and apparently available, we would like to know what to say, and we might rehearse a line or two to break the ice. What do you think is appropriate, and what do you think is shallow and a turn off? Test your thoughts on this by writing examples of "good," "mediocre," and "shallow" opening lines in the space below. Then tell a friend what you are up to, and ask him or her to evaluate the examples you have written.

Follow-Up Questions:

1.   How well did you do? Was your friend able to tell correctly what your intentions were?

2.   Generally, what goals do you recommend people try to achieve with their opening remarks to someone they find attractive?

3.   What do people of the opposite sex report are appropriate for opening lines? Ask your classmates or friends for ideas. If you cannot ask others, try to imagine what they would say. Write down what you can and ask your instructor to provide some feedback or class discussion.

Name _____ Date _____

13.2   It May Be in How We Say It

While the suave lines we invent to initiate relationships are important, the nonverbal cues we give may be even more significant. Try to imagine you are a screenwriter working on a movie. You are writing a line for the heroine or hero, whomever you identify with, who is approaching the other star for the first time, and simply says: "Good evening," or alternatively "Hi, my name is _____." Now write the stage direction, referring to vocal tone, eye contact, bodily postures, and movement.

1.   First, write this for yourself.

2.   Second, write this for someone who is very shy.

3.   Finally, write this for your favorite actor or actress.

4.   Describe how the president says this before a televised talk.

Follow-Up Questions:

1.   What did you rely on most for creating different nonverbal communication in this activity?

2.   What would you most like to change about your own nonverbal communication?

13.3   It May Be When We Say It

After initial attraction, we are still "on approval," meaning we still want to keep Mr. or Ms. "Right" favorably impressed with us. In our first and early testing opportunities, we can, and likely must, disclose information to each other. Rathus and Nevid point out how we must consider what is safe to disclose and what could be self-damaging and prematurely revealing. Consider the research project discussed in Chapter 13, where researchers had their confederates reveal intimate information early in a ten-minute conversation, or late in the conversation, and as a consequence either come across as immature and phony if they revealed too early, or more attractive when revealing the same information toward the end of the ten minutes.

Write down three items of disclosure you think the researchers could have used in their study to create the effects they found.

1.

2.

3.

You will need some feedback on how well you did, so share your three ideas with your confidant, your class, or your instructor. Be prepared for some criticism because these are judgment calls. Others may have a less than adequate idea of the context you have imagined. Let's hear them out because we are at least being sensitized to some of the relevant points the textbook is trying to make. How did you do?

13.4 A Tall Job

A tall job is what Rathus and Nevid call the preparation of a marriage contract, even an informal one. But to avoid ending up like the Trumps, let us do it anyway. Consider each of the eleven issues discussed in the questions below, and decide how each would be resolved for you.

1. What name will the wife use after marriage?

2. How will chores be allocated?

3. Will there be children, and if so how many and when?

4. Will there be contraception, and if so what kind?

5. How will child care be distributed?

6. Whose career will determine where you live?

7. Who will work and who will decide financial decisions?

8. Which relatives will be visited and how often?

9. What leisure activities will be shared and unshared?

10. How will sexual issues be decided, and what will the decisions be?

11. How can changes in this contract be accommodated?

12. Do you agree with some experts who believe marriages should be free of such contractual specifications?

14

Sexual Behavior

14.1   The Perfect Sex Questionnaire

In this chapter we learn how reliant we are on information from surveys and questionnaires to understand sexual behavior. We also learn that many questionnaires are open to some methodological flaws, or are dated, or just didn't ask the "right" people. There is only one way to find the "perfect sex questionnaire." You will have to write it. Try writing five relevant questions about sexual behavior that would answer questions that are important to you. They may reflect a concern, or an issue related to your interests.

1.

2.

3.

4.

5.

Your instructor may wish to follow up this activity with class discussion.

Name _____ Date _____

14.2   Sex and Entertainment

The last movie or television show you saw that included sexual intimacy will serve as our target for this activity. The answers may tell us much about the attitudes and behaviors being encouraged today.

1.   Did the script suggest that safe sex was being practiced?

2.   What kind of relationship was the couple involved in? Was it a long-term relationship, such as a marriage or cohabitation, or a brief fling, or what?

3.   Was the relationship intact at the end of the movie?

4.   Do you think there are different standards of sexual behavior for yourself, for others, or for entertainment?

14.3 What Are Your State's Laws?

The laws governing sexual behavior differ from state to state. Occasionally we read about obviously outdated laws that are still on the books, but not enforced. Missouri once had a law forbidding a woman from refusing her husband's sexual advances.

What does your state say about the following sexual issues? Answer a) what you believe the law says, and then b) find a good source for the law to check yourself.

1.   What is your state's age for statutory rape?

    a)

    b)

2.   Is homosexuality legal in your state?

    a)

    b)

3.   Does your state allow cohabitation or recognize common law marriage?

    a)

    b)

4.   Does your state require a blood test for a marriage license, and if it does, is AIDS included in the screening?

    a)

    b)

5. Which of the laws are not enforceable?

6. Would you like to see any of these laws changed? Why?

Name _____ Date _____

14.4   Critical Thinking

Researchers have found evidence that rape victims tend to be less dominant and less self-assertive than nonvictims. The results suggested that women who appear to be vulnerable are more likely to be attacked. If we look critically at this research, we will see that it is a bit premature to conclude that women have been socialized into the role of victims who are "asking for it."

1.   What other explanations could account for research findings such as this?

2.   What kind of study could more successfully test the hypothesis that being less dominant and self-assertive could increase the risk of being a rape victim?

111

15

Adult Development:
Going Through Changes

15.1   Where Are You?

From the discussion in this chapter, where would you place your current development? In what ways is your experience consistent with the discussion, and in what ways is your experience inconsistent with the discussion?

1.   Current development:

2.   Consistent experiences:

3.   Inconsistent experiences:

15.2   Our Parents as Subjects

Consider one or both of your parents for a while. Where are they in terms of their adult development? Would they tend to nod agreeably if they were reading this chapter, or would they look puzzled or even openly disagree?

1.   Try to create their reaction in your mind and describe it.

2.   This might be a good time to call home and check out your attempt to empathize with either or both parents. What can it accomplish? What will they say to these questions?

        a.   When in their lives did they experience the greatest amount of freedom?

        b.   When did they experience the greatest physical change?

        c.   When did they feel most in control of their lives?

        d.   What changes do they look forward to?

        e.   What could you add to this set of questions?

15.3   Getting Ready for the Rest of Life

Support groups help us through so many of life's experiences. There are support groups in our locale for victims of diseases, former patients of various disorders, survivors of suicide, and parents who experience the loss of a child. There are also informal social supports we enjoy when lunching with colleagues, bowling with friends, or talking over the fence with a neighbor.

Where will we get support for growing older and dealing with the challenges of aging? Will we just have to laugh at ourselves as our eyes lose their focus, our waistlines fight for space, and our children's tuition bills come due? It may be that the most reliable support will come from within ourselves.

Taking Shakespeare's dictum that "nothing is either good or bad, thinking makes it so," reword the following changes that can come with aging so that the glass is half full instead of half empty, so to speak.

> "The first half of life consists of the capacity to enjoy without the chance; the last half consists of the chance without the capacity."
>
> Mark Twain

1.   Please calculate your life expectancy (from Chapter 15), and imagine you discovered you have just passed the halfway point of your predicted lifespan. Will this be the half of life described by Mark Twain as the "half that consists of chance without the capacity?" How could the last half be described in positive language?

2.   Suppose you are holding the newspaper at arm's length and still squinting to read the print which you feel "isn't as good as it used to be." If you give in to nature and start wearing glasses, you would be showing your age. How could this turn of events be described positively?

3. Soon there will be no child living in your home. Growing up and moving out is creating the "empty nest." What can be positive about this?

4. Of all the challenges or changes outlined in this chapter, what one would you add to this activity? How could you reconstruct it in a more positive light?

5. What is the next major life change you anticipate? Consider the chapter discussion relevant to your age and use it to compare or contrast this next major life change, again, viewing it in a positive light.

6. Identify one change or challenge in this chapter that you will **not** be experiencing because of your abilities, beliefs, strengths, or choices. How will it be possible to avoid this one?

118

Name _____ Date _____

15.4   Aging and Stereotypes

Television and movie writers often take advantage of stereotypes about aging, and thereby contribute to some of the myths surrounding it. Please identify an example of ageism that is perpetuated by entertainment, and bring your example to class to contribute to a discussion.

1.   Describe your example here.

2.   In contrast, illustrate a case where the writer has helped provide some accurate insight.

119

16

The Challenge of the Workplace

16.1   Resources for Career Information

There are some fantastic resources waiting at your library that can provide important information about the career you have chosen or are considering. You will find the reference librarian very helpful and able to direct you to titles such as *The Dictionary of Occupational Titles* and *The Occupational Outlook Handbook*. The latter is updated yearly and is quite complete in coverage of the nature of occupations. Both titles are widely held at libraries designated as Federal Depository Libraries and generally are available at local, regional, and campus libraries. Ask the person behind the reference desk for directions, and answer the following questions about your chosen career, or what you might consider for a career.

1.   What is the nature of the work? Does it seem to fit your preconceptions?

2.   What work conditions are associated with the occupation?

3.   How many people are currently employed in this occupation?

4.   What training and other qualifications are required?

5.   What is the outlook for this career choice?

6.   What earnings and advancement opportunities are associated with this career choice?

7.   What health benefits are associated with this job?

8.   Is your interest in this career enhanced or reduced by this activity? What exactly was influential?

9.   Which stage of vocational development is associated with this activity?

10.   If you won the lottery, would you still choose this career?

Name _____ Date _____

16.2   Our Work and Our Identity

The textbook points out the tendency for us to say "I am a _____" rather than "I work as a _____," and thus, we intertwine career with self-identity. We will be or already are sensitive at those times people ask us what our major is, what our career plans are, and what work we do.

Ask three people who are unfamiliar with your career interests to grade the "prestige" they associate with five jobs that you identify, including your first choice. Use a scale of 1 to 10, with 10 being the most prestigious job. Also ask each participant to give an example of a job they would rate a 1 and one they would rate a 10.

Follow-Up Questions:

1.   Is it alarming or comforting to learn what others think of your choice?

2.   How much did the three judgments vary?

3.   Do the opinions of others regarding your career choice have any value to you?

125

16.3   Supercharging Your Formal Education

It is hard to find it in writing, but students generally know that there are courses outside of their major, called electives, that are extremely useful, exciting, and valuable.

1.   What courses could you describe to your class that you would highly recommend?

2.   Ask a friend for his or her recommendation for an elective course and the reason for the recommendation.

3.   Please bring these to class for sharing, and indicate which class or classes intrigue you.

Name _____ Date _____

16.4   What Matters on the Job?

Since most of us have work experience, we can judge the relative contribution of several of the components that influence job satisfaction or dissatisfaction. Rank each item from 1 to 5, with 1 representing the most important and 5 representing the least important. Briefly explain your rating.

1. _____ The boss

2. _____ Geographic location

3. _____ Fellow workers

4. _____ Environment

5. _____ Hours

Follow-Up Questions:

1. This is an activity that is also good to share with other members of your class. It probably would be useful to discover what your classmates' experiences are, especially if they are quite different from your own. For example, working nights or weekends might not be part of your experience, so the insights of others might be valuable if you are thinking of a career in a medical field.

2. Given the possible effects of criticism, goal setting, linkage of pay to productivity, work redesign, flextime, and stress at the workplace, how would you change the workplace you rated in this activity?

3. How would you monitor, measure, and document improvements that your recommendations could create?